ROYAL BOTANIC GA

CW00541751

Field Key to

O Wild RCHIDS *of* Scotland

PATRICK WOODS AND MARY BATES

EDINBURGH : HMSO

HMSO publications are available from:

HMSO Bookshops
71 Lothian Road, Edinburgh, EH3 9AZ
031-228 4181 Fax 031-229 2734
49 High Holborn, London, WC1V 6HB
071-873 0011 Fax 071-873 8200 (counter service only)
258 Broad Street, Birmingham, B1 2HE
021-643 3740 Fax 021-643 6510
Southey House, 33 Wine Street, Bristol, BS1 2BQ
0272 264306 Fax 0272 294515
9-21 Princess Street, Manchester, M60 8AS
061-834 7201 Fax 061-833 0634
16 Arthur Street, Belfast, BT1 4GD
0232 238451 Fax 0232 235401

HMSO Publications Centre
(Mail, fax and telephone orders only)
PO Box 276, London, SW8 5DT
Telephone orders 071-873 9090
General enquiries 071-873 0011
(queuing system in operation for both numbers)
Fax orders 071-873 8200

HMSO's Accredited Agents
(see Yellow Pages)
and through good booksellers

ISBN 0 11 495105 5

Field Key to
Wild Orchids of Scotland

Patrick Woods and Mary Bates

When identifying an orchid, several points should be borne in mind. Flowers, although they may vary in minor details such as intensity of colour, are the most reliable feature. Plants in exposed situations are often smaller than those in, for example, sheltered positions or in tall vegetation. Pigmentation, particularly the reddish colour from anthocyanins in stems and ovaries, is affected by light levels, usually being stronger in brighter light. Scent can not only be a rather subjective character but can also be influenced by the age of the flower, whether pollination has taken place, the weather, and even the time of day. Dactylorchids are difficult to separate, particularly at subspecies level, and further complications arise because they hybridise freely. Here geographic and habitat differences may be useful. *Epipactis youngiana* and *E. leptochila* var. *dunensis* are very similar in appearance and are insufficiently known in Scotland to be identified with certainty.

We have followed the most widely accepted current nomenclature, but the correct application of names and the taxonomic rank of some of the dactylorchids is still a matter of debate among botanists.

This key is based entirely on Scottish plants, which differ in some minor respects from material from other parts of Britain.

2a

2b

6a

6b

1a. Plants without green leaves _____2
1b. Plants with green leaves _____3

2a. Plants robust, entirely creamy-brown
or straw-coloured, to 52cm tall;
inflorescence many-flowered, crowded;
lip c.12mm long, deeply cleft into
2 lobes, honey-brown, unspotted
10. Neottia nidus-avis
2b. Plants slender, yellowish or reddish, to 28cm
tall; inflorescence 4–13-flowered,
not crowded; lip c.5mm long, shallowly
3-lobed, white with crimson spotting
towards base _____ *13. Corallorhiza trifida*

3a. Lip with spur _____4
3b. Lip without spur _____26

4a. Spur distinctly longer than ovary,
slender _____5
4b. Spur as long as or shorter than ovary,
not slender _____10

5a. Lip strap-shaped, not lobed; flowers always
white or greenish white, sweetly scented; leaves
2, rarely more, sub-opposite, broad elliptic to
ovate _____6
5b. Lip lobed; flowers usually bright pink or reddish
purple, rarely white, pleasantly or unpleasantly
scented; leaves several, not sub-opposite,
lanceolate or oblong _____7

6a. Petals curving round to form a semi-circular
hood over column; pollinia divergent; entrance to
spur clearly seen
17. Platanthera chlorantha
6b. Petals forming a loose triangular hood over
column; pollinia parallel; entrance to spur not
clearly seen _____*18. Platanthera bifolia*

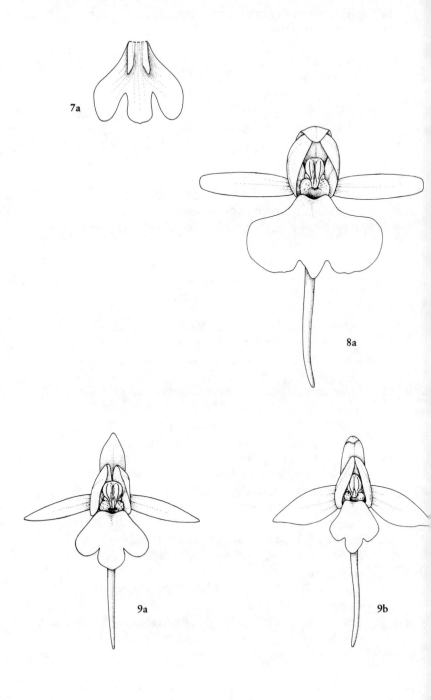

7a

8a

9a

9b

7a. Inflorescence conical, less so when mature, with slightly unpleasant foxy smell; lip deeply 3-lobed with 2 plate-like ridges at base; leaves grey-green _____*28. Anacamptis pyramidalis*

7b. Inflorescence cylindrical, sweetly scented; lip with 3 rounded lobes, not ridged at base; leaves shiny bright green _____8

8a. Lip much broader than long, with 'shoulders', side-lobes larger than mid-lobe; lateral sepals blunt at tips, held horizontally; spicy clove scent. Damp habitats
15b. Gymnadenia conopsea subsp. *densiflora*

8b. Lip as long as or slightly longer than broad, side-lobes equal to or smaller than mid-lobe; lateral sepals pointed at tips, angled downwards; scent slightly acidic or of carnations. Drier habitats _____9

9a. Lip with 3 almost equal lobes; lateral sepals linear; scent with acidic overtones. Dry limestone areas
15a. Gymnadenia conopsea subsp. *conopsea*

9b. Lip with side-lobes shorter than mid-lobe, lobes sometimes hardly noticeable; lateral sepals oval-lanceolate; carnation-scented. Hill pastures
15c. Gymnadenia conopsea subsp. *borealis*

10a. Flowers creamy or greenish white or greenish, or suffused brownish or purplish; lip with 3 apical lobes _____**11**

10b. Flowers purplish, reddish or rarely white; lip not as above _____**12**

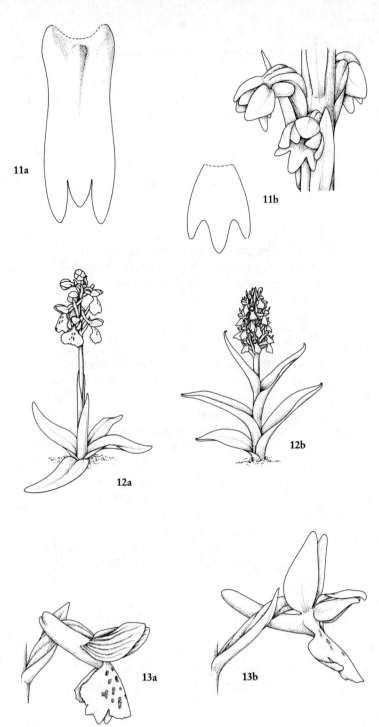

11a

11b

12a

12b

13a

13b

11a. Flowers greenish, often suffused brownish or purplish, not bell-shaped, not downward facing; lip strap-shaped, the mid-lobe much smaller than side-lobes; spur almost globular; faintly honey-scented _____ *14. Coeloglossum viride*

11b. Flowers creamy or greenish white, bell-shaped, downward facing; lip as broad as long, the mid-lobe longer and broader than side-lobes; spur short, blunt, conical; faintly vanilla scented _____ *16. Pseudorchis albida*

12a. Basal leaves in a rosette, upper leaves clasping stem for almost their whole length; bracts somewhat membranous, 1–2 mm wide, often reddish _____ 13

12b. Leaves not arranged as above, upper leaves not clasping stem; bracts ± leaf-like, 3–5mm wide _____ 14

13a. Stem 6–15cm tall; inflorescence 3–12-flowered; lateral sepals angled forward, distinctly green-veined, sepals and petals forming a loose hood; lip broader than long, 3-lobed to almost entire, mid-lobe not longer than side-lobes; leaves not purple marked; usually sweetly scented _____ *19. Orchis morio*

13b. Stem 8–46cm tall; inflorescence many-flowered; lateral sepals angled upward, not distinctly veined, dorsal sepal and petals forming a loose hood; lip as broad as long, 3-lobed, mid-lobe longer than side-lobes; leaves of most plants with elongated purple blotches; often smells of tom-cats, occasionally sweetly scented
20. Orchis mascula

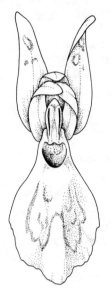

14a

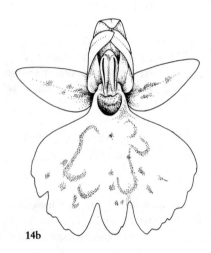

14b

16a

16b

14a. Lateral sepals angled upwards, often touching back to back; sides of lip usually reflexed to some extent; spur over 2mm diameter; flowers flesh pink, dark red, magenta to purple; leaves purple marked or not; non-sheathing leaves few, usually 1, occasionally to 3; lower floral bract more than 3mm wide _____ **15**

14b. Lateral sepals spreading or angled below the horizontal; side-lobes of lip not reflexed; spur less than 2mm in diameter; flowers predominantly whitish or pinkish, sometimes darker pink or reddish purple, or white; leaves usually purple marked; non-sheathing leaves to 3 or more; lower floral bract no more than 3 mm wide _____ **23**

15a. Plants slender; lower sheathing leaves linear to lanceolate, tips not hooded; bracts purplish, purple-marked or not; inflorescence lax; flowers magenta-purple, magenta-red, magenta-pink or lilac _____ **16**

15b. Plants usually robust; lower sheathing leaves lanceolate to ovate-lanceolate, tips hooded or not; bracts green, reddish or purplish, rarely purple-marked; inflorescence dense; flower colour as above or flesh colour or pink _____ **17**

16a. Sheathing leaves 2–3, heavily blotched or spotted, purple-edged; non-sheathing leaves 0–2; bracts purple-marked on both sides; flowers magenta-purple or magenta-red, rarely lilac; lateral sepals erect and blunt with dark markings; lip markings strong and intense dark violet-purple
26. Dactylorhiza lapponica

16b. Sheathing leaves 2–5, almost always 3, usually unmarked, or if purple-marked then in upper $1/3$ only; non-sheathing leaves 0–1; bracts unmarked; flowers magenta-purple to magenta-pink or lilac; lateral sepals upward spreading and pointed, faintly marked; lip marked with dots and lines, not intense nor tending to violet
27. Dactylorhiza traunsteineri

17a

18a

19a

17a. Sheathing leaves ± erect, hooded at tips, usually yellowish green, usually without purple marks, if marked then on both sides of leaf; non-sheathing leaves 0–1; flowers flesh-pink, dark red, magenta to purple; lip unlobed or not deeply lobed, sides usually reflexed _____ **18**

17b. Sheathing leaves ± spreading, not hooded at tips, not yellowish green, blotched, spotted or unmarked, if marked then on upper surface only; non-sheathing leaves 1–2; flowers bright magenta-purple to pinkish purple; lip broad, flat, distinctly or indistinctly 3-lobed, mid-lobe small _____ **21**

18a. Flowers pale lilac-purple to violet-magenta; lip not deeply lobed but mid-lobe usually prominent, side-lobes not strongly reflexed; leaves purple-spotted on both sides; fleck markings on upper stem, bracts and ovaries. NW Scotland
23d. _Dactylorhiza incarnata_ subsp. **_cruenta_**

18b. Flowers flesh-pink, reddish purple, magenta to deep crimson; lip shallowly lobed to entire, mid-lobe not prominent, side-lobes strongly reflexed; leaves not purple-marked; upper stem, bracts and ovaries without flecks _____ **19**

19a. Flowers flesh pink; plant 7–50cm tall, rarely more than 20cm. Marshy areas
23a. _Dactylorhiza incarnata_ subsp. **_incarnata_**

19b. Flowers reddish purple, magenta to deep crimson; plant usually less than 20cm tall _____ **20**

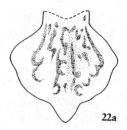

22a

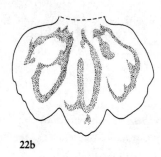

22b

20a. Flowers bright crimson to madder red; short stout plants 8–15cm tall; leaves thick, dark green, fairly broad, strongly keeled and hooded. Dune slacks and moist dune grassland, rarely a short distance inland
23b. Dactylorhiza incarnata subsp. *coccinea*
20b. Flowers mauve-purple or magenta; plants to 30cm tall; leaves pale green, narrow, not strongly keeled. Mainly in acid boggy areas
23c. Dactylorhiza incarnata subsp. *pulchella*

21a. Sheathing leaves 3, sometimes 4, crowded towards base, markings varying from smallish blotches to a complete purple-brown colouration, can be purple-edged; inflorescence not flat topped; flowers violet-purple; lip broad, distinctly 3-lobed. N Uist and possibly Jura
24. Dactylorhiza majalis subsp. *scotica*
21b. Sheathing leaves usually 4 or more, not crowded at base, unmarked or purple-marked; inflorescence flat-topped; flowers bright purple to pinkish purple or magenta; lip diamond-shaped or not deeply lobed. Widespread _____**22**

22a. Leaves unmarked or occasionally with very small spots, usually towards apex; bracts unspotted; lip tending to be diamond-shaped; flowers bright purple to magenta. Widely distributed
25a. Dactylorhiza purpurella subsp. *purpurella*
22b. Leaves usually with round purple blotches, often large, and usually over entire upper surface; bracts spotted or very rarely unspotted; lip tending to be 3-lobed; flowers pinkish purple. Outer Hebrides, N and NW coasts
25b. Dactylorhiza purpurella subsp. *majaliformis*

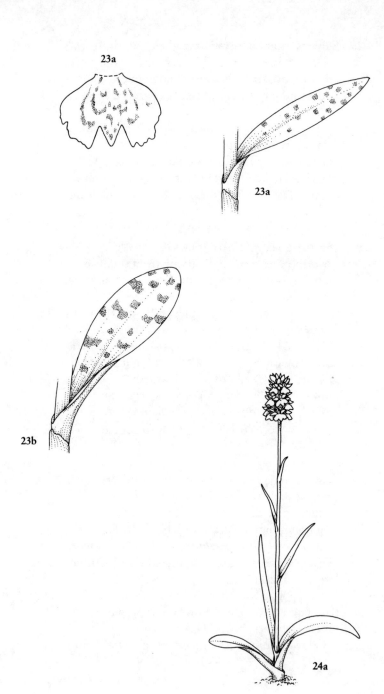

23a

23a

23b

24a

23a. Plants slender; leaves lanceolate, usually with
round pale purplish spots; lowest leaf shorter but
not wider than others, tip pointed; inflorescence
few-flowered, ± pyramidal; flowers white to
pinkish lilac, normally pale; mid-lobe
of lip usually shorter than conspicuous
side-lobes; spur 1mm wide. Acid soils and
heathland
  22. Dactylorhiza maculata** subsp. **ericetorum

23b. Plant usually but not always robust; leaves
narrow to broad, usually with dark transversely
elongated blotches, or unmarked, lowest leaf
shorter and wider than the others, tip rounded;
inflorescence few- to many-flowered, short to
long and tapering; flowers pale lilac to rosy
purple, rarely white; mid-lobe of lip longer than
side-lobes; spur 1–2mm wide. Mostly on
alkaline soils, sometimes open woodland ____24

24a. Slender plants 12–20cm, rarely taller; leaves
narrow and unmarked; flowers white,
occasionally with faint markings; sweetly
scented. SW Scotland and Inner Hebrides
  21c. Dactylorhiza fuchsii** subsp. **okellyi

24b. Stout plants 6–70cm tall; leaves usually purple-
marked; flowers palest pink to rosy purple (very
occasionally ± white); scarcely scented _____25

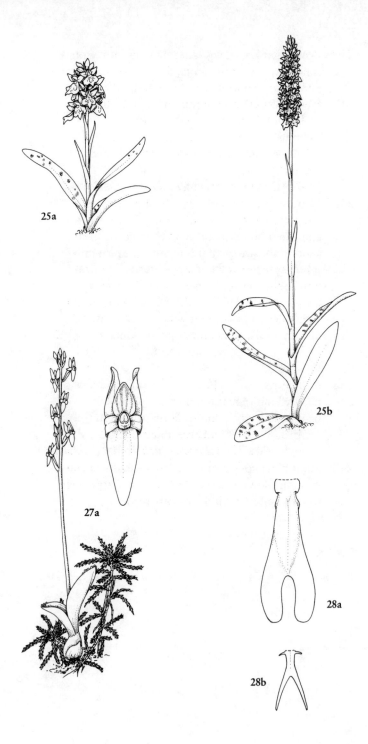

25a

25b

27a

28a

28b

25a. Plants usually to 20cm tall; inflorescence compact; flowers rose-pink to deep lilac; leaves usually blotched, often densely. Hebrides, Shetland, and NW coast of Scotland
21b. Dactylorhiza fuchsii subsp. *hebridensis*
25b. Plant 17–70cm tall; inflorescence elongated, cylindrical to tapering; flowers pale to deep pinkish purple (rarely white); leaves usually marked with transversely elongated blotches. Widely distributed
21a. Dactylorhiza fuchsii subsp. *fuchsii*

26a. Leaves arising below middle of stem; upper part of stem bare _____27
26b. Leaves spaced along length of stem _____29

27a. Plant very small and slender, to 10cm tall; leaves to 1cm long, arising at or near swollen stem base; flower minute, yellowish green; lip uppermost, triangular, unlobed. Wet sphagnum bogs
12. Hammarbya paludosa
27b. Leaves 2 (rarely 3), sub-opposite, arising in lower half of stem but not at the unswollen base; lip lowermost, strap-shaped, deeply cleft into 2 lobes, sometimes also with 2 small side-lobes near base _____28

28a. Robust plant, 10–60cm or more tall; leaves 5–20cm long, oval; inflorescence of numerous greenish flowers; lip reflexed, lobes rounded at tips _____*8. Listera ovata*
28b. Slender plant to 24cm tall; leaves 1–2.5cm long, heart-shaped or oval; inflorescence of 3–15 reddish green flowers; lip not reflexed, lobes pointed at tips _____*9. Listera cordata*

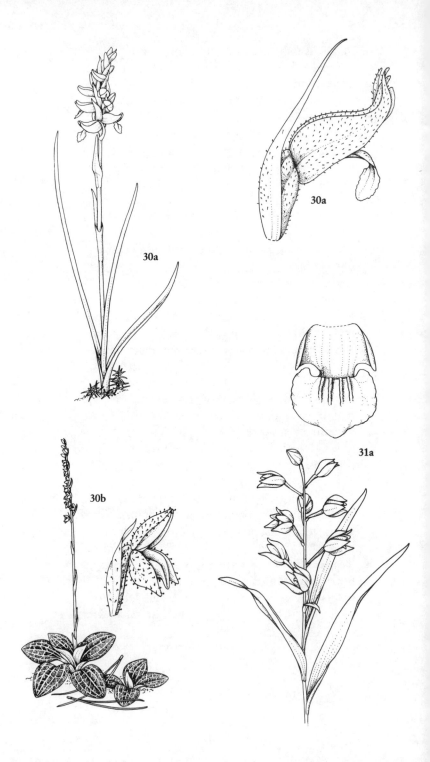

30a

30a

31a

30b

29a. Flowers crowded, ± spirally arranged, glandular hairy, white or creamy-white; lip not divided into 2 parts by a joint or hinge _____ **30**

29b. Flowers not crowded, sometimes with downy hairs, never entirely white; lip divided into 2 parts: the apical part or epichile separated from the basal part or hypochile by a narrow fold or hinge _____ **31**

30a. Plants not creeping; leaves long, narrow and erect; inflorescence stout, 2–4 x 2cm; flowers in 3 spiral rows; apical edges of lip frilled and toothed; strongly hawthorn-scented. Mainly in damp places in W Scotland and the Hebrides
7. Spiranthes romanzoffiana

30b. Plants creeping, ± mat forming; leaves in a loose basal rosette and some way up stem, evergreen, stalked, ovate, usually conspicuously net-veined; inflorescence slender, 5–7 x 1cm; flowers in a single spiral row, twisted so that they tend to face the same direction; lip pointed at tip, sac-like at base; sweetly scented. Pinewoods in N and E Scotland _____ *11. Goodyera repens*

31a. Loose inflorescence of 3–40 white flowers tending to face upwards or horizontally; bracts, except sometimes lower one or two, tiny; sepals and petals not widely spreading; base of epichile with several basal orange ridges; ovary unstalked; leaves lanceolate to linear lanceolate
1. Cephalanthera longifolia

31b. Loose inflorescence of 7–60 greenish, purplish or brownish flowers, tending to face horizontally or downwards; bracts not tiny; sepals and petals widely spreading or not; base of epichile with boss-like swellings; ovary stalked; lower leaves ovate to elliptic _____ **32**

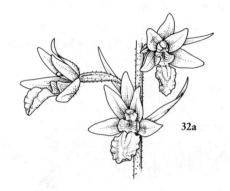

32a

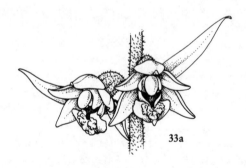

33a

32a. Inflorescence of 7–14 showy flowers; sepals with short hairs outside, brownish or purplish green, paler inside; petals whitish suffused pink or purplish; lip white, as long as or longer than sepals and petals; epichile with frilled upturned margins and yellow-edged boss at base, connected by a narrow hinge to lobed, reddish veined hypochile. Marshy places

2. Epipactis palustris

32b. Inflorescence of 3–60 not very showy flowers, purplish, greenish or greenish suffused purplish or pinkish; lip shorter than sepals and petals; epichile without frilled margins, connected to hypochile by a fold. Dryish open places or in woodland _____ 33

33a. Flowers wine-red or purplish, very rarely cream; epichile with reflexed tip and 3 prominent basal bosses, hypochile green with red margin; upper stem and ovary densely downy; lower leaves usually suffused purplish on underside. Restricted to limestone areas

6. Epipactis atrorubens

33b. Flowers not wine-red or cream, if purplish always suffused green, sometimes pinkish or whitish green; epichile with 2 or 3 basal bosses; upper stem and ovary hairy (not downy) or glabrous; leaves not suffused purplish on under surface. Not restricted to limestone areas _____ 34

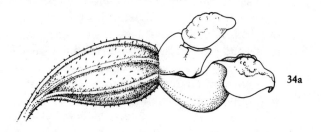

34a

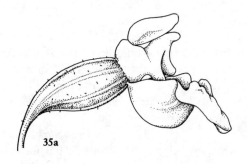

35a

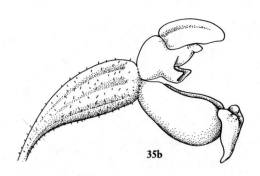

35b

34a. Plants usually large and robust; inflorescence of up to 60 drooping flowers, greenish flushed purplish or pink; epichile broader than long with reflexed tip and 2 rough basal bosses, hypochile dark brownish inside; pollinia remaining intact unless removed by an insect; leaves dark green, strongly ribbed underneath, lowest one broader than long _____*3. Epipactis helleborine*

34b. Plants usually slender; inflorescence of up to 20 greenish, yellowish green or pink-tinged flowers; pollinia disintegrating in situ; leaves yellowish green, weakly ribbed underneath, lower ones longer than broad _____35

35a. Sepals 8–11mm long, greenish, the margins usually faintly rose-coloured or white; petals greenish with rose margins; rostellum as long as anther; ovary sparsely short hairy or glabrous
4. Epipactis youngiana

35b. Sepals 6–8mm long, sepals and petals yellowish green; rostellum not more than half length of anther; ovary with short hairs
5. Epipactis leptochila var. *dunensis*

Notes

Notes

Notes

Notes

Notes

Notes

Notes

Printed in Scotland for HMSO by (3808)
Dd 287891 C30 4/93